Ride with Emilio

Ride with Emilio

Written and illustrated
by Richard Nares

Ride with Emilio

Published by Dave Burgess Consulting, Inc.

San Diego, CA

DaveBurgessConsulting.com

Library of Congress Control Number: 2020945148

Paperback ISBN: 978-1-951600-61-7

Illustrations by Richard Nares

Design by Liz Schrieter

Editing and production by Reading List Editorial: readinglisteditorial.com

To my wife, Diane, and Emilio,
who is always my inspiration.

This is a story about a little boy named Emilio. Like all parents, when his mom and dad brought him home from the hospital, they were bursting with happiness and excitement.

His parents showered him with
love and plenty of attention.

When Emilio's mom and dad went to work, Tía Rosa and Emilio would travel from one end of their San Diego neighborhood to the other.

When Emilio began walking at nine months,
a whole new world opened up.

One of Emilio's favorite things to do was
to take long walks with his mom and dad.

As Emilio grew, he found the world was full of fun things to discover, even in his own backyard.

Shortly after his third birthday, Emilio came down with a fever. His parents took him to the doctor, who decided to run some blood tests.

When the results came back,
the doctor had very bad news.
With tears running down his
face, he told Emilio's parents,
"Emilio has leukemia."

Although Emilio was in remission within the first thirty days of treatment, he spent many days in the hospital not feeling well.

On his good days, Emilio was able to return to preschool. His teacher helped him and his classmates understand what cancer is and is not.

On his good days, Emilio loved to ride his bike, play baseball with his dad, and go to the beach.

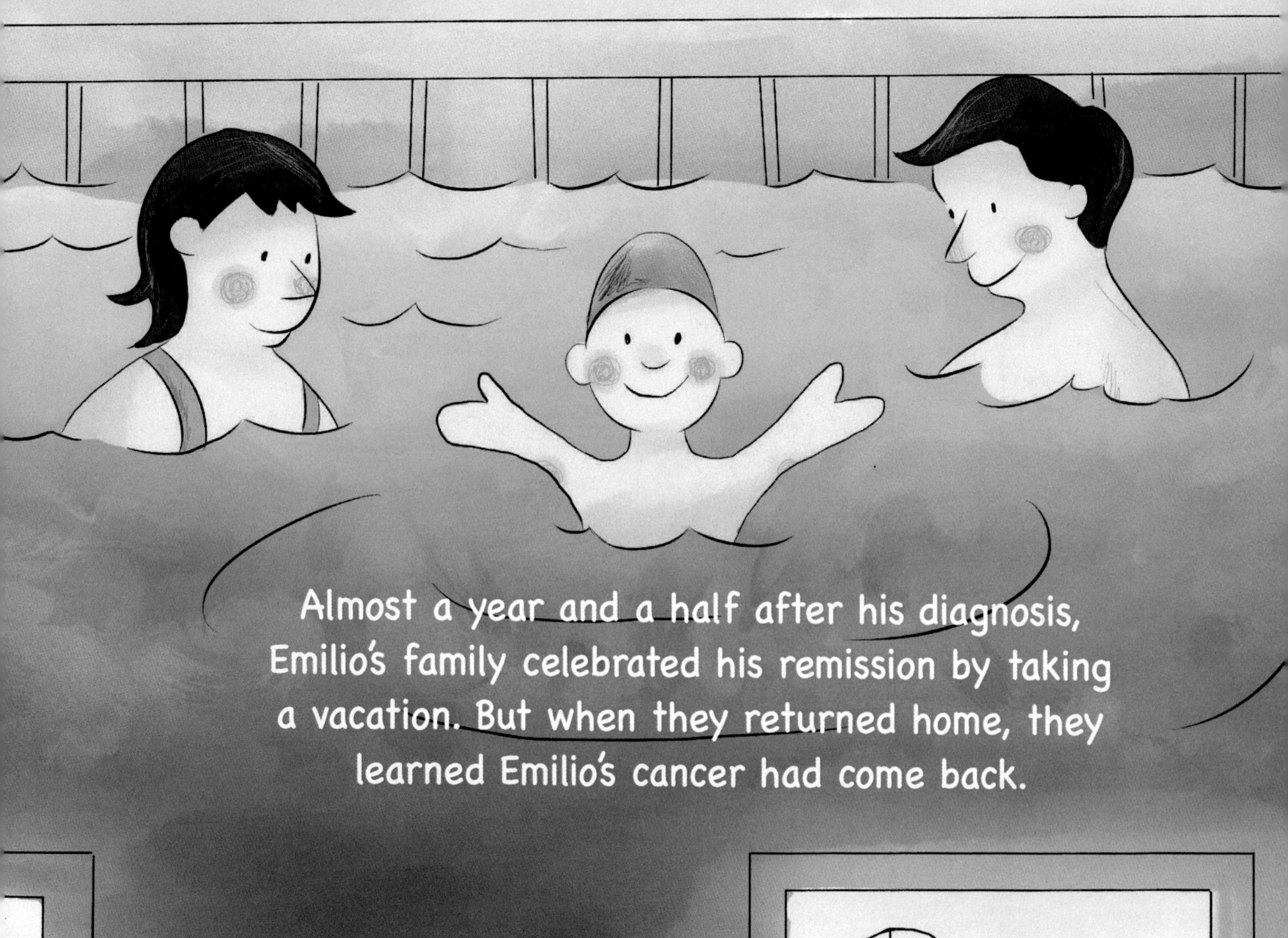

Almost a year and a half after his diagnosis, Emilio's family celebrated his remission by taking a vacation. But when they returned home, they learned Emilio's cancer had come back.

Emilio and his parents took a big trip all the way to the East Coast so that Emilio could receive a bone marrow transplant at Boston Children's Hospital. While there, he got to see the Boston Red Sox play at Fenway Park.

But after his treatment, Emilio didn't feel better. The cancer wouldn't leave his body.

After almost three years of battling leukemia, Emilio died on a chilly Sunday morning in the fall. His mom and dad were at his bedside in Boston.

Emilio's mom and dad were devastated, but over time, a little bit of light returned to their faces. They began to smile again. Emilio's dad even started volunteering at the hospital where Emilio had received treatment.

As he talked to other parents, Emilio's dad realized just how fortunate their family had been. Because they had reliable transportation, he and his wife had always been able to take Emilio to his many doctor's appointments. This, he learned, was not possible for all families.

Sometimes children missed their cancer treatments because the family car was unreliable. And sometimes a family couldn't afford to have a car, and they had to rely on the bus.

The bus ride to the hospital sometimes took hours, and sometimes this made kids miss their appointments. What's more, taking public transportation is dangerous for children with suppressed immune systems.

Emilio's dad decided to do something. Using his own car, he began driving children and their parents to and from the hospital to help make sure they always got their treatment.

After two months and many requests for rides, Emilio's parents realized that they needed a more permanent solution. So, they started Ride with Emilio, a free transportation program.

One day, wherever there's a children's hospital, the Emilio Nares Foundation will be there to ensure that no child ever has to miss their cancer treatment due to lack of transportation.

CHILDREN'S
HOSPITAL
MAIN ENTRANCE
Ride with Emilio

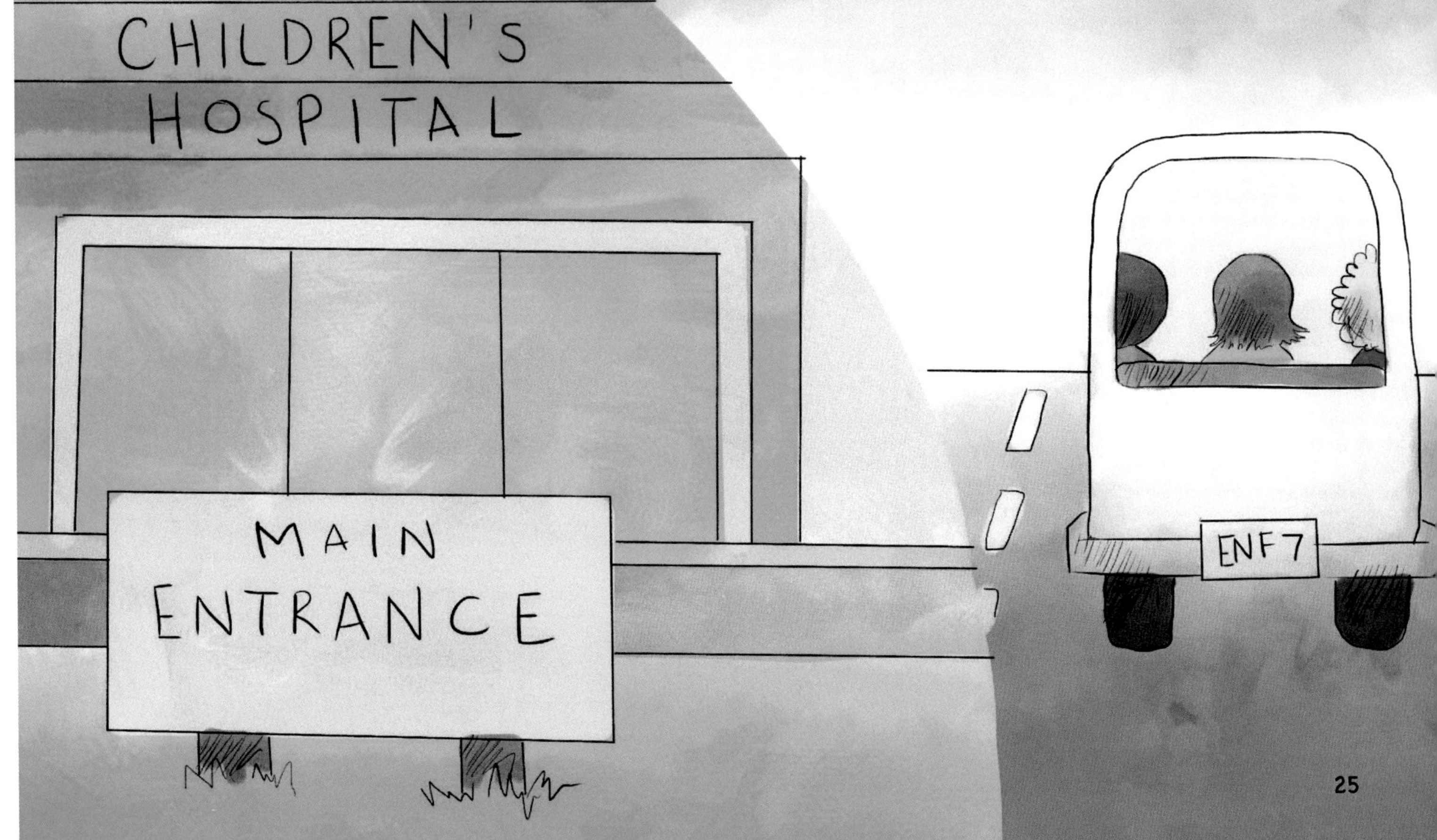
CHILDREN'S
HOSPITAL
MAIN
ENTRANCE
ENF7

Ride with Emilio
ENF7

Today Emilio's spirit can be felt in the hundreds of children the Emilio Nares Foundation helps each year. Whenever there's laughter in the van, a smile between friends, or a hug on a hard day, we know Emilio is looking after us all.

For more information, please visit enfhope.org.

Besides providing transportation, we offer several other services.

Classes

Free sewing, knitting, and crocheting classes are great therapy and create a sense of community among families in a similar situation.

Resource Center

We help families access information on housing, employment, financial aid, and their child's cancer treatment.

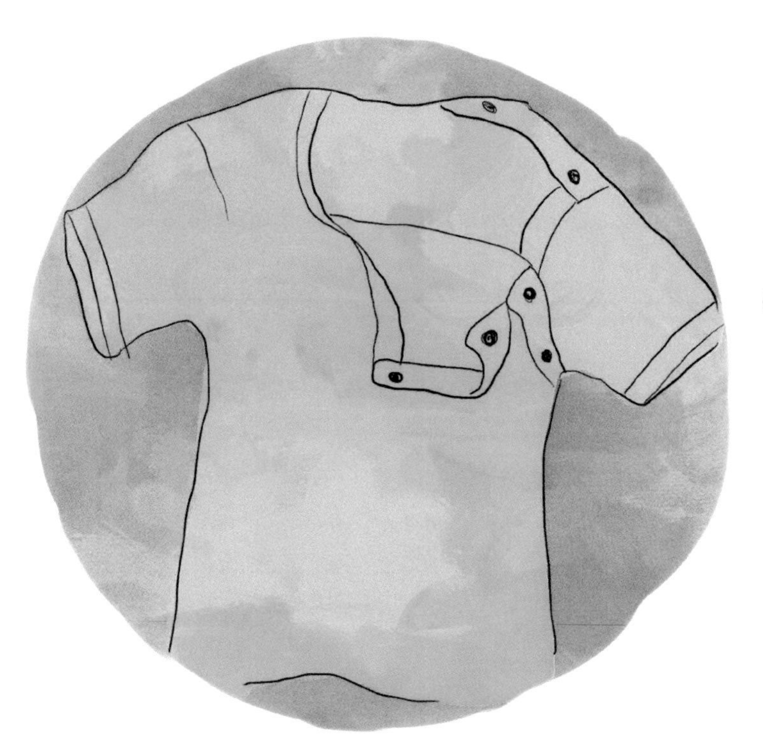

Emilio's Loving Tabs

Specially designed shirts enable nurses to access the catheter port in a patient's chest to deliver chemotherapy and other medications. Thanks to the design of our shirt, a child does not have to lift or remove their shirt, which reduces stress and fear and helps them to be more comfortable.

Snack Bags

We provide free nutritious snack bags to children who are recovering from chemotherapy treatments.

Afterword:
Ride with Emilio is a love story.

Diane and Richard Nares met, fell in love, and married around the age of 40. Not long after that, they were blessed with a beautiful baby boy. Their son, Emilio, brought even more love to their lives. Eventually, this profound love would propel his legacy to touch more lives than either of them could have ever imagined.

The Emilio Nares Foundation (ENF) provides unique and life-enhancing services to thousands of disadvantaged families, as these families travel their own difficult journey of childhood cancer. ENF's positive impact in the world has been widely recognized. To name two examples, during the Major League Baseball All-Star Game in 2009, President Obama presented Richard Nares as the *People* magazine and Major League Baseball Top All-Star Among Us recipient. In 2013 Richard was honored as one of CNN's Top 10 Heroes.

In the fall of 2000, I was in Emilio's Boston hospital room when he looked out the window and asked his dad about the crowds in the street. Richard told him about the Jimmy Fund Walk, which follows the course of the Boston Marathon. Emilio asked his dad if he would run the Boston Marathon for him someday. Richard, who had never before been a runner, immediately responded, "Sure, Emilio. I'll do that for you." Within a year, Richard had run his first marathon. It would take him twelve marathons to finally qualify for Boston, an event he has now successfully completed three times. In 2018, to raise awareness and funds for ENF, Richard ran from Seattle to San Diego, stopping at every children's hospital along the way. When I asked him how he manages to keep going during these often lonely mega-runs, he smiled and said, "Emilio encourages me and pushes me forward, every minute of every run."

This is the story of a love that has proved to be far more powerful than a parent's grief, a boy's life that would improve the lives of thousands of strangers.

—John Cappetta, Emilio's uncle

Richard Nares

Acknowledgments

Thank you to Angelica Lopez for the colorization of my illustrations.

To Dave & Shelley Burgess, at Dave Burgess Consulting, Inc., thank you for giving me the opportunity to tell my story and to introduce the world to the Emilio Nares Foundation.

Thank you, Lindsey Alexander, for your kindness, patience, and professionalism.

Made in the USA
Las Vegas, NV
25 October 2020